THE LORD OF

SUMALI WAS THE KING OF THE RAKSHASAS.
FROM THE NETHER-WORLD, WHERE HE LIVED,
HE ONCE CAME TO VISIT THE WORLD OF MEN,
ALONG WITH HIS BEAUTIFUL DAUGHTER, KAIKESI.

YOU SHALL MARRY THE WORTHIEST OF MEN AND BEAR MANY MIGHTY SONS.

HE TRAVELLED FROM ONE PLACE TO ANOTHER LOOKING FOR THE MAN. BUT–

KAIKESI, NOT ONE OF THEM IS GOOD ENOUGH.

AT LAST, ONE DAY, HE SAW A MAGNIFICENT CHARIOT DESCENDING FROM THE SKY IN FRONT OF THE HERMITAGE OF VISHRAVA, A GREAT SAGE.

THAT IS KUBERA, VISHRAVA'S SON. HOW NOBLE IS HIS BEARING! HE SEEMS RICH AND MIGHTY.

SUMALI RETURNED WITH HIS DAUGHTER TO THE NETHER-WORLD; BUT HE COULD NOT FORGET KUBERA.

DAUGHTER, APPROACH VISHRAVA. AND WIN HIM OVER. IF HE MARRIES YOU, YOU WILL HAVE SONS AS MIGHTY AS KUBERA.

ACCORDINGLY KAIKESI WENT TO THE HERMITAGE OF VISHRAVA. HE WAS BUSY OFFERING HIS EVENING PRAYERS.

O BEAUTIFUL MAIDEN! WHO ARE YOU? WHY HAVE YOU COME HERE?

MY NAME IS KAIKESI. YOU ARE A GREAT SAGE. YOU KNOW WHY.

I UNDERSTAND. BUT YOU HAVE COME TO ME AT THE WRONG HOUR. THE CHILDREN BORN TO US WILL BE WICKED RAKSHASAS...

3

LORD!

...THE YOUNGEST HOWEVER WILL BE A NOBLE ONE.

VISHRAVA MARRIED KAIKESI AND WITHIN A FEW YEARS, RAVANA, THE TEN-HEADED ONE, KUMBHAKARNA, SHOORPANAKHA, AND VIBHEE-SHANA WERE BORN.

YEARS ROLLED BY. RAVANA AND KUMBHAKARNA GREW UP TO BE ARROGANT AND AMBITIOUS. ONE DAY, KUBERA CAME TO VISIT HIS FATHER.

AFTER KUBERA HAD LEFT—

RAVANA, MY SON! LOOK AT KUBERA, THE KING OF LANKA. HE IS RICH AND POWERFUL. YOU MUST BE LIKE HIM.

MOTHER, HERE AND NOW I MAKE THIS VOW. I WILL EXCEL KUBERA.

RAVANA IMMEDIATELY SET OUT FOR GOKARNA ALONG WITH HIS BROTHERS, KUMBHAKARNA AND VIBHEESHANA. THEY BEGAN PERFORMING SEVERE PENANCES.

DURING THE PENANCE, RAVANA DID NOT TOUCH FOOD. ONE BY ONE HE SACRIFICED HIS HEADS IN THE HOLY FIRE.

WHEN HE WAS ABOUT TO SACRIFICE HIS TENTH HEAD, LORD BRAHMA APPEARED BEFORE HIM.

I AM PLEASED WITH YOU. ASK FOR A BOON.

5

BRAHMA ALSO GRANTED BOONS TO VIBHEESHANA AND KUMBHAKARNA.

VIBHEESHANA, WHAT BOON DID LORD BRAHMA GRANT YOU?

IMMORTALITY. I HAD ONLY EXPRESSED THE WISH THAT I MIGHT NEVER SWERVE FROM THE PATH OF RIGHTEOUSNESS.

AND WHAT A FOOL I WAS! I ASKED FOR SLEEP FOR MANY YEARS.

WHEN THEY RETURNED HOME, SUMALI CAME TO MEET THEM.

RAVANA, I AM PROUD OF YOU. NOW WIN BACK LANKA. IT BELONGS RIGHTFULLY TO OUR PEOPLE.

PROMPTED BY THE WORDS OF SUMALI AND HIS MEN, RAVANA SET OUT FOR LANKA.

BROTHER! IT IS NOT PROPER.

QUIET, VIBHEESHANA. WHO ASKED FOR YOUR ADVICE?

FROM HIS CAMP IN THE JUNGLE OF THE TRIKOOTA MOUNTAINS, RAVANA SENT A MESSENGER TO THE COURT OF KUBERA.

GO AND TELL KUBERA THAT HE MUST VACATE LANKA, IMMEDIATELY. I WISH TO OCCUPY IT.

AT THE COURT OF KUBERA—

WHY DOES HE ASK ME TO VACATE LANKA? AFTER ALL, WHAT IS MINE IS HIS.

TELL RAVANA, I WILL CONSULT MY FATHER AND ACT.

KUBERA WENT TO VISHRAVA.

FATHER, TELL ME WHAT I SHOULD DO.

BRAHMA'S BOON HAS MADE RAVANA EVEN MORE ARROGANT. AGREE TO HIS WISH. GO TO MOUNT KAILAS. YOU WILL PROSPER THERE.

KUBERA VACATED LANKA. RAVANA CAME THERE WITH HIS ARMY AND BECAME THE KING.

AS THE DAYS PASSED, RAVANA BECAME INCREASINGLY ARROGANT. HE BEGAN HARASSING THE GODS, SAGES AND GANDHARVAS.

WHEN THE NEWS REACHED KUBERA—

RAVANA'S BEHAVIOUR IS BAD. IT IS MY DUTY TO CORRECT MY YOUNGER BROTHER.

HE SENT A MESSENGER TO LANKA.

MY MASTER, KUBERA SAYS, IT DOES NOT BEFIT THE RACE OF VISHRAVA TO HARASS SAGES AND KILL INNOCENT PEOPLE. YOU MUST MEND YOUR WAYS.

IMPUDENT MAN! YOU WILL PAY FOR THIS.

NOW I MUST TEACH KUBERA THE LESSON OF HIS LIFE.

MOUNTING HIS CHARIOT AND ACCOMPANIED BY A MIGHTY ARMY, RAVANA SPED TOWARDS KAILAS, KUBERA'S KINGDOM.

A GREAT BATTLE TOOK PLACE BETWEEN THE ARMIES OF RAVANA AND KUBERA.

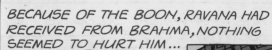

BECAUSE OF THE BOON, RAVANA HAD RECEIVED FROM BRAHMA, NOTHING SEEMED TO HURT HIM...

...NOT EVEN THE MIGHTY MACE OF KUBERA.

AT LAST KUBERA FELL...

...BUT THE GODS WHO WERE WITNESSING THE BATTLE FROM ABOVE, TOOK HIM TO SAFETY IN A HEAVENLY CHARIOT.

THERE WAS NONE TO OBSTRUCT RAVANA NOW. HE SEIZED 'PUSHPAK', THE FLYING CHARIOT OF KUBERA, AND BEGAN EXPLORING MOUNT KAILAS.

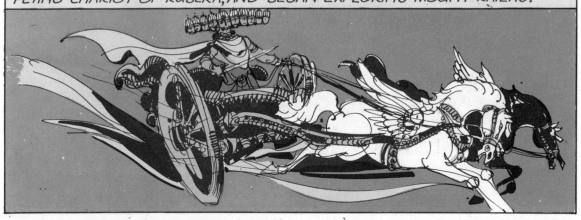

SOON, HOWEVER, 'PUSHPAK' CAME TO A DEAD HALT.

WHEN RAVANA SAT BROODING ABOUT THE CAUSE...

...NANDI, SHIVA'S ATTENDANT, CAME DOWN.

RAVANA! THIS IS LORD SHIVA'S ABODE. DO NOT DISTURB HIM.

WHOSE ORDERS ARE THESE? SHIVA'S? I'LL UPROOT THIS VERY MOUNTAIN ON WHICH HE RESTS.

ASSUMING A HUGE FORM RAVANA TRIED TO LIFT KAILAS.

AS THE MOUNTAIN SHOOK, THE FOLLOWERS OF SHIVA WERE TERRIFIED.

O LORD! HELP! SAVE US!

EVEN PARVATI, LORD SHIVA'S CONSORT, WAS SCARED.

LORD!

DO NOT FEAR. I'M HERE.

LORD SHIVA PRESSED THE MOUNTAIN WITH HIS TOE AND RAVANA'S HANDS WERE CRUSHED BELOW IT.

AHH! HELP!

RAVANA'S MINISTER ADVISED HIM.

NONE OTHER THAN LORD SHIVA CAN SAVE YOU NOW. PROPITIATE HIM.

RAVANA BEGAN SINGING HYMNS IN PRAISE OF SHIVA.

PLEASED WITH HIM, LORD SHIVA PERMITTED RAVANA TO REMOVE HIS HANDS FROM UNDER THE MOUNTAIN...

...AND GAVE HIM A SWORD.

RAVANA! YOU ARE A MIGHTY WARRIOR.

RAVANA NOW ROAMED ABOUT THE WORLD, CONQUERING ALL WHOM HE MET.

ONE DAY, IN THE JUNGLES OF THE HIMALAYAS, HE SAW A BEAUTIFUL MAIDEN ENGAGED IN MEDITATION.

RAVANA ADVANCED TOWARDS HER.

O BEAUTIFUL MAIDEN, WHO ARE YOU? WHY DO YOU PERFORM SUCH AUSTERITIES?

I AM VEDAVATI. I AM PERFORMING THESE AUSTERITIES TO WIN LORD VISHNU AS MY HUSBAND.

I AM RAVANA, LORD OF LANKA. MARRY ME.

NONE OTHER THAN VISHNU CAN BE MY HUSBAND. GO AWAY.

RAVANA SEIZED HER BY HER HAIR.

ENRAGED, VEDAVATI CREATED A FIRE...

...AND JUMPED INTO IT.

I WILL BE BORN AGAIN AND BE THE CAUSE OF YOUR DEATH.

VEDAVATI TOOK BIRTH IN A LOTUS.

WHAT A BEAUTIFUL BABY! WHO COULD SHE BE?

RAVANA TOOK HER TO HIS CAMP. BUT—

SHE WILL BE THE CAUSE OF YOUR DEATH.

WHAT SHALL I DO WITH HER?

DISCARD HER.

RAVANA IMMEDIATELY THREW HER INTO THE RIVER.

MANY DAYS LATER, IN KING JANAKA'S YAGNASHALA,* AT MITHILA—

BEFORE I BEGIN THIS FIRE SACRIFICE, I HAVE TO TILL THE SOIL SYMBOLICALLY.

SUDDENLY THERE APPEARED, IN THE CENTRE OF THE HALL, A BEAUTIFUL CHILD.

MY PRAYERS HAVE AT LAST BEEN ANSWERED. I'LL ADOPT HER AS MY CHILD.

IT WAS NONE OTHER THAN VEDAVATI.

SINCE I HAVE OBTAINED HER FROM A FURROW** I'LL NAME HER SITA.

SITA SOON GREW TO BE A BEAUTIFUL GIRL LOVED BY ONE AND ALL.

* HALL OF FIRE-SACRIFICE.   ** SITA.   18

JANAKA ARRANGED A SWAYAMWARA TO WHICH HE INVITED PRINCES FROM FAR AND NEAR.

HE WHO SUCCEEDS IN STRINGING THIS BOW WILL WIN SITA'S HAND.

AMONG THE PRINCES WAS RAMA. OF AYODHYA, WHO HAD COME THERE WITH SAGE VISHWAMITRA.

RAMA LIFTED THE BOW EASILY. IT BROKE UNDER HIS STRENGTH.

HE MARRIED SITA AND CAME WITH HER TO AYODHYA WHERE THE PEOPLE WELCOMED THEM WARMLY.

MEANWHILE —

NOW I MUST CONQUER THE GODS IN HEAVEN.

SAVE US!

20

ONE NIGHT, WHEN RAVANA AND HIS MEN WERE RESTING ON MOUNT KAILAS, NEAR KUBERA'S CAPITAL ...

...HE SAW A BEAUTIFUL MAIDEN PASSING BY.

HE GOT UP FROM HIS SEAT AND STARTED MOVING TOWARDS HER.

22

RAMBHA TREMBLED.

I LOVE NALKOOBER, THE SON OF KUBERA, YOUR STEP-BROTHER. WE WILL SOON BE MARRIED.

RAVANA SEIZED HER BY HER ARM.

YOU SHALL MARRY ME.

BUT RAMBHA ESCAPED FROM HIS CLUTCHES. SHE WENT TO NALKOOBER AND NARRATED ALL.

RAVANA DARED TO THINK OF MARRYING YOU. IF HE EVER MARRIES A WOMAN AGAINST HER WILL, HIS HEADS WILL BREAK INTO SEVEN PIECES.

WHEN RAVANA HEARD THIS—

WHO IS AFRAID OF A WEAKLING'S CURSE?

BUT IN HIS HEART OF HEARTS HE TREMBLED.

YET, HE DID NOT STOP BEING WICKED.

ONE DAY, RAVANA CAME, DISGUISED AS A MONK, TO THE DANDAKA FOREST.

O BEAUTIFUL ONE, WHO ARE YOU? WHAT ARE YOU DOING HERE, ALONE IN THIS FOREST?

I AM SITA, WIFE OF RAMA, THE PRINCE OF AYODHYA. HE HAS GONE HUNTING...

...MY HUSBAND HAD TO COME TO LIVE IN THE FOREST TO FULFIL A PROMISE MADE BY HIS FATHER. WHO ARE YOU?

I AM RAVANA. I HAVE COME HERE TO TAKE YOU WITH ME. YOU WILL BE MY WIFE.

NEVER! GIVE UP SUCH THOUGHTS. YOU WILL ONLY INVITE DEATH BY COVETING ME.

UNDAUNTED RAVANA ASSUMED A HUGE FORM.

HE LIFTED HER...

...AND BROUGHT HER IN HIS CHARIOT TO LANKA.

AFTER HE HAD PLACED HER IN HIS ASHOKA GARDEN UNDER GUARD —

I LOVE YOU. WHY DO YOU WASTE YOUR TIME ON RAMA, WHO HAS BEEN BANISHED FROM HIS KINGDOM? MARRY ME.

RAVANA! YOUR DAYS ARE NUMBERED. MY LORD WILL SOON COME HERE AND KILL YOU.

ENRAGED, RAVANA ADVANCED TOWARDS HER...

...BUT FEAR KEPT HIM AWAY.

NO. NALKOOBER'S CURSE MAY COME TRUE. I MUST NOT MARRY A WOMAN AGAINST HER WILL.

MEANWHILE, RAMA WAS ON HIS WAY TO LANKA. HE HAD REACHED THE SHORE OF THE OCEAN WITH A HUGE ARMY OF MONKEYS AND BEARS.

RAVANA CALLED HIS BROTHERS AND COURTIERS.

WE MUST FIGHT AND KILL RAMA AND HIS ARMY.

BROTHER! IT IS ONLY PROPER THAT YOU RETURN SITA TO RAMA. HE WILL GO BACK IN PEACE.

RAVANA WAS ANGRY WITH VIBHEESHANA.

YOU CANNOT BEAR TO SEE MY MIGHT. YOU ARE A DISGRACE TO THE FAMILY. IF YOU WERE NOT MY BROTHER I WOULD HAVE KILLED YOU.

VIBHEESHANA, WITH FOUR OTHER RAKSHASAS FLEW INTO THE SKY...

...AND CAME TO THE CAMP OF RAMA.

RAMA! I SEEK YOUR PROTECTION.

YOU WILL BE SAFE HERE. I COUNT ON YOUR HELP.

SOON A BRIDGE WAS CONSTRUCTED ACROSS THE OCEAN AND...

...RAMA REACHED LANKA.

RAVANA BECAME IMPATIENT WITH SITA.

LISTEN, SITA! RAMA IS NO MORE. HE LIES DEAD IN THE BATTLEFIELD.

I DON'T BELIEVE YOU.

RAVANA TURNED TO ONE OF HIS WARRIORS.

GO AND FETCH THE HEAD OF RAMA.

WITHIN MINUTES, THE HEAD OF RAMA LAY IN FRONT OF SITA.

NOW, ARE YOU CONVINCED THAT RAMA IS DEAD? AND THIS IS HIS BOW. DON'T YOU RECOGNISE IT?

SITA, SHOCKED AT THE SIGHT, FELL UNCONSCIOUS.

WHEN SHE CAME BACK TO HER SENSES...

MY LORD! DEAD! WHAT SHALL I DO?

JUST THEN —

LORD! THE COMMANDER OF YOUR ARMY WANTS TO MEET YOU URGENTLY.

THE MOMENT RAVANA LEFT, RAMA'S HEAD AND BOW DISAPPEARED.

HOW DID THEY DISAPPEAR?

RAVANA DECEIVED YOU BY HIS MAGIC. DON'T GRIEVE, SITA. RAMA IS NOT DEAD.

RAMA WAS VERY MUCH ALIVE. LANKA WAS SOON CONVERTED INTO A BATTLEFIELD.

ONE BY ONE, THE WARRIORS OF RAVANA FELL.

THE MIGHTY KUMBHAKARNA PLAYED HAVOC ON THE MONKEY ARMY. BUT HE TOO FELL.

RAVANA HOWEVER CARRIED ON THE BATTLE.

WHEN HE FELL—

MY BROTHER! HOW I WISH YOU HAD HEEDED MY WORDS! YOUR PRIDE BROUGHT ABOUT THIS FALL.

DON'T GRIEVE, VIBHEESHANA! HE HAS DIED LIKE A BRAVE WARRIOR.

LANKA NOW HAD A NEW LORD—THE GOOD AND GENTLE VIBHEESHANA. RAMA HAD HIM CROWNED KING.

AFTER THE CROWNING OF VIBHEESHANA, RAMA RETURNED WITH SITA TO AYODHYA.